The character of John Constantine was created by Alan Moore,
Stephen Bissette and John Totleben.

HELLBLAZER VOLUME THREE
ISBN 1 85286 251 3
Published by Titan Books Ltd
58 St Giles High St
London WC2H 8LH

First British edition, January 1990
10 9 8 7 6 5 4 3 2 1

Cover illustration by Dave McKean
This edition designed by Rian Hughes
Printed and bound in Great Britain
by Richard Clay Ltd, Bungay, Suffolk

HELLBLAZER

VOLUME THREE

Written by JAMIE DELANO and RICK VEITCH
Drawn by JOHN RIDGWAY, RICK VEITCH,
RICHARD PIERS RAYNER and TOM MANDRAKE
Inked by ALFREDO ALCALA and MARK BUCKINGHAM

TITAN BOOKS

BIOGRAPHIES

JAMIE DELANO

First commissioned, in 1983, to write the *Nightraven* text stories in *Marvel Superheroes*, Jamie was soon writing *Captain Britain* and *Dr Who*, all for Marvel UK. In 1985 he began writing *Future Shocks* for Fleetway's *2000 AD*, until being offered *Hellblazer* in 1987. This he still writes, and has also penned the six part series, *World Without End*.

JOHN RIDGWAY

John began his career in 1967 by drawing short tales for 'library' format war comics. Since 1981, he has drawn several series for Warrior's *Quality* and Marvel UK and several one-off episodes, plus a graphic novel — *The Agent* — published in 1989 for Marvel US. His *Hellblazer* was executed in 1987-88. For Fleetway he has drawn *Judge Dredd* and *Summer Magic* and is now drawing *The Dead Man*.

RICHARD PIERS RAYNER

Richard's 1985 self-published work *Solthenis* sufficiently impressed DC editor Karen Berger to persuade her to hand him the drawing chores on *Hellblazer* in 1988. Since then he has drawn *Swamp Thing* and *L.E.G.I.O.N. 89* annuals for DC and *Third World War* for Fleetway's *Crisis*.

RICK VEITCH

An adaptation of the movie *1941* was Rick's first professional work, for *Heavy Metal*. *Heartburst*, a graphic novel for Marvel, followed in 1984, and *Abraxas and the Earthman* and *The One* for Epic. His work on *Swamp Thing* from 1986-89 is his best known and he has now formed a company, King Hell, to publish, among other works, his own series *The Brat Pack*.

TOM MANDRAKE

After graduating from Joe Kubert's School of Cartoon and Graphic Art, Tom's first comics work was in 1980-81 on DC war titles. *New Mutants*, for Marvel in 1982, gave way to *Arion* and *Batman* for DC, *Grimjack* for First Comics and *Swamp Thing* for DC again. He is now working on *Firestorm* for DC and *Classics Illustrated* titles for First/Berkeley Books.

ALFREDO ALCALA

1948 marked the start of Alfredo's comics career, with *Aksiyon* and *Filipino* comics in the Philippines. Since 1971 he has worked for DC and Marvel from his home in California. He has illustrated such titles as *Conan*, *The Hulk*, *Man-Thing*, *Batman*, *Kamandi*, *The Shadow* and *Swamp Thing*, which he continues to ink.

MARK BUCKINGHAM

From his 1987 debut in *Strip AIDS*, *Heartbreak Hotel* and *The Truth* magazine, Mark soon became the inker on *Hellblazer*, graduating to pencils after a few issues. He has since teamed up with writer Neil Gaiman to produce a new *Miracleman* series for Eclipse.

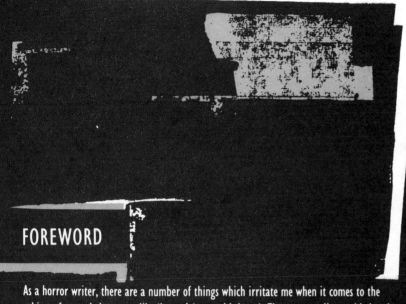

FOREWORD

As a horror writer, there are a number of things which irritate me when it comes to the subject of central characters like 'heroes' (a word I detest). They are usually troubled and cynical, but with hearts of gold beneath their granite-hard exteriors. They make you sick. 'Where have all the bastards gone' to rephrase a line from the song? — I'll tell you where one of them is: he's cutting a swathe through *Hellblazer*.

John Constantine, psychic investigator, can sometimes appear to be one of the biggest bastards you're likely to encounter in horror fiction, and I welcome him because of that. Let's face it, the guy has problems. It's his very fallibility which makes him so human, his frailty of character which makes him such a wonderfully complex creation. Constantine is Philip Marlowe without compassion. He's Sam Spade without integrity. In the mould of a private detective but with a freshness and sly humour so apt for this and many ages to come.

The stories in *Hellblazer* Volume Three all contain the essential elements of horror fiction such as shock, terror and violence, but they also contain an element all too rarely used: dark comedy. My own personal favourite is *Sex and Death* (two subjects close to my own heart!) mainly because it contains all the previously mentioned elements in abundance. There is also a savage beauty to the illustrations which complement the occasionally searing dialogue.

There's a well-worn phrase in the rock music business to describe something exceptional: 'It kicks ass!' *Hellblazer* Volume Three kicks with both feet. And it kicks hard!

Shaun Hutson
July 1989

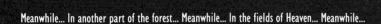

Meanwhile... In another part of the forest... Meanwhile... In the fields of Heaven... Meanwhile...

One of the ways in which comics grew up, in the end, was in the assumption of continuity, the assumption that the actions of these characters, no matter how caped or monstrous, had consequences, consequences that might jump out at them, years later. Things come back to haunt them, and us.

When Alan Moore introduced John Constantine, the street-cred sorcerer (told in *Swamp Thing* Volume Five) to be a foil to a Swamp Thing that had become increasingly an elemental force of nature, it was to oppose the City to the Forest and the Swamp, the manipulator of people and power to the embodiment of the Green, which bends with the wind. When they fought alongside, it was against forces of Chaos and Old Night hostile to both their worlds. And that fight, and the way Constantine used the Swamp Thing as his secret weapon against the Brujeria (told in *Swamp Thing* Volume Eight), left them with debts to settle and reckonings to be made...

As this volume of *Hellblazer* opens, both have new problems. The Swamp Thing's extended absence in interstellar space has automatically created the germ of a new Elemental, the Sprout; his return left it incomplete, redundant and dangerous — but Swamp Thing has never been one to kill the innocent when there was another way.

Constantine has found himself caught between Heaven and Hell; between the deranged fundamentalists of the Tongues of Fire and the slug-tongued demon Nergal and his Damnation Army, trusting neither. The fundamentalists have taken back his girlfriend Zed, whom they intend to be the Mary, mother of a Twentieth Century Messiah, and have killed his gay friend Ray Monde. Nergal has raised Constantine from his sickbed by contaminating him with demon blood, but he is not a man to feel he owes favours, or to take any side except his own.

Here are major problems, with Constantine and the Swamp Thing as two mutually suspicious heroes to solve them, pay old debts, and discover older ones...

This volume contains two issues of *Hellblazer* and two cross-over issues of *Swamp Thing*. Continuity gets a little complicated here, since the first half of the second *Hellblazer* story (Chapter Three) runs concurrently with the first of the two *Swamp Things* (Chapter Two), and the second *Swamp Thing* (Chapter Four) takes place between pages 81 and 82, near the end of the second *Hellblazer*, before Constantine catches the plane back to London. This is a volume that stacks up a lot of meanwhiles.

As far as the payment of debts goes, it is probably worth noting that the first of these *Swamp Thing* stories, *L'Adoration de La Terre*, has a title making clear that Rick Veitch, its writer, is paying homage to Alan Moore, from whom he had taken over on the series. Here, Swamp Thing and Abby make love in a human way; in Moore's classic *Rite of Spring* (*Swamp Thing* Volume Four), they consummated their love rather differently. And, as ballet fans among you may know, *The Adoration of the Earth* is the second section of Stravinsky's ballet, *The Rite of Spring*. The payment of debts gets very complicated.

Roz Kaveney
September 1989

CHAPTER ONE

SHOT TO HELL

HEY, RAGGEDY MAN. I SEEN A SPACEMAN IN THE AUTOMAT.

HE GAVE ME A GOLD PRETZEL--

--BUT I LOST IT.

KONKRUMSH!

PSSS! PSS PSS PSS!

FAGGOT!

KONKRUMSH!

YEAH?

MAY 10 Gotham B

1 IN 61 BABIE
H.I.V. POSITIV

PRETTY BAD HEADLINE, EH?

I DUNNO. I WAS LOOKING AT THE *DATE*.

T'S MY SODDIN' BIRTHDAY, ENNIT?

I'M THIRTY-FIVE YEARS OLD -- AND TOTALLY...

"SHOT TO HELL"

JAMIE DELANO, WRITER • JOHN RIDGWAY & ALFREDO ALCALA, ARTISTS

TODD KLEIN, LETTERER • KAREN BERGER, EDITOR

3

CUH-CONGRATULATIONS.

HAPPY BIRTHDAY, DEAR BOY.

BEEN CELEBRATING, THEN?

HEY MAN, Y'BETTER SIDDOWN-- BEFORE Y'FALL.

JESUS. YOU SHOULD LOOK AT YOURSELF, JOHN. YOU'RE DISGUSTING -- ROTTEN DRUNK, STINKING.

SO?

WHAT'S IT TO YOU LOT? YOU'RE ALL BLOODY DEAD! HAH!

FIFTEEN MEN ON ON A DEADMAN'S CHEST--

YO HO HO AND A BOTTLE OF RUM.

YEAH...

DRINK TO THE DEVIL AND BE DONE WITH THE REST...

QUIET DOWN, YA LOONY TOON!

GODDAMN LIMEY WEIRDO!

THAT'S THE PROBLEM, ISN'T IT, JOHN CONSTANTINE? YOU'VE TASTED SATAN'S HEADY BREW -- AND IT'S TEMPTED YOU.

TASTED IT, YOU BLOODY STUPID NUN -- IT'S FLOWING IN MY *VEINS*.

AND Y'KNOW WHAT? *I* DON'T GIVE A *TOSS!*

WHAT'S THAT?

LISTEN, YOU STUTTERING PRATT. DON'T GIVE ME THAT *MARTYR* CRAP.

WHAT DO YOU THINK IT'S LIKE FOR *ME?*

I'M HAUNTED HALF TO BLOODY DEATH. EVERYBODY WANTS *MY* ARSE -- THE *LAW*, THE *ELEMENTALS*, HEAVEN, HELL.

AND *IF* I STAY AHEAD OF ALL OF THEM -- WHAT'S THE *FUTURE* GOT FOR *ME?*

KOFF! KOROFF!

A BED ON THE *CANCER WARD* -- IF THERE'S A NATIONAL HEALTH SERVICE LEFT BY THEN.

I'M *TIRED.* DO YOU UNDERSTAND? THE CARDS ARE BLOODY RUBBISH --

-- I'M CASHING IN MY CHIPS.

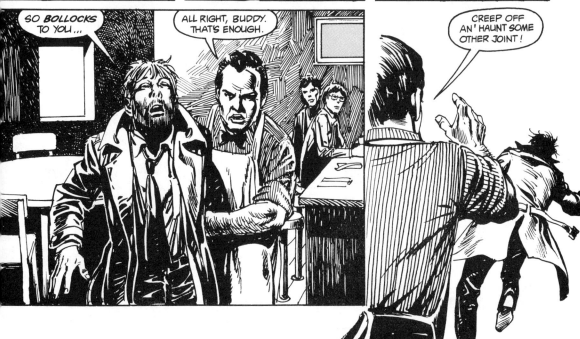

SO *BOLLOCKS* TO YOU...

ALL RIGHT, BUDDY. THAT'S ENOUGH.

CREEP OFF AN' HAUNT SOME OTHER JOINT!

JOHN, WAIT! YOU'RE NOT ALONE. I KNOW HOW YOU FEEL.

OH BLOODY *DO* YOU?

WHEN I FOUND OUT I HAD *AIDS*, I FELT TOTALLY ALONE -- UNCLEAN.

A PARIAH WHO COULD NEVER AGAIN TOUCH A THING OF BEAUTY WITHOUT FEAR OF CORRUPTING IT.

FROM ME, THE MOST POTENT ACT OF *LOVE* COULD BE THE TOUCH OF *DEATH*.

WHAT'S THAT GOT TO DO WITH ME?

THE *DEMON BLOOD* HAS TRIGGERED A SORT OF *PSYCHIC AIDS* IN YOU.

DON'T DESTROY YOURSELF, JOHN. DON'T LET *SELF-PITY* POISON YOU.

AT LEAST YOU HAVE *LOVE* TO HOLD ON TO.

BALLS. WHAT LOVE?

THERE'S *ZED*, JOHN. *SHE* LOVES YOU. AND DON'T TELL ME YOU DON'T CARE FOR *HER* --

SHUT UP!

--YOU'RE NOT EVEN SODDIN' REAL.

--I KNOW YOU *DO*.

SHUT UP, YOU MISERABLE OLD FRUIT. YOU KNOW *NOTHING* --

KONKRUMSH!

DAY AFTER FUGITIVE DAY; FOOTSTEP AFTER SHUFFLING FOOTSTEP; HEARTBEAT AFTER ANXIOUS HEARTBEAT--

KRONKLIMSH

--MY ENEMIES HUNT ME DOWN.

DOWN TO THE ROCKY BOTTOM OF THIS SUNKEN CITY'S RUINED HEART.

I AM AN UNDERWATER MAN.

HIDING; SQUEEZED INTO DARKNESS; A KITTEN IN A WEIGHTED SACK--TOO TIRED TO STRUGGLE, I NURSE THE BLOATED TEAT OF DROWNED DESPAIR.

I DRIFT.

BUT TERROR WILL NOT LET ME CLOSE MY EYES.

DRIP

WRIGGLING, ELECTRIC, REAL; IT NUZZLES ME; LIQUID, SINUOUS AS AN EEL--

DRIP DRIP

--LIKE MERCURY.

--OR OIL.

GWWLOOMP

9

KONKRUMMSH

NO REST.

LAST NIGHT THE WOMAN IN THE ROOM NEXT TO MINE SOBBED 'TIL DAWN. I COULD'VE *KILLED* HER.

TODAY, WOUNDED SKY LEAKS ONTO A COLLAPSING WORLD--SOON THERE'LL BE NOWHERE LEFT TO HIDE.

I WALK, A SWOLLEN AGONY OF FEET-- PAIN KEEPS ME MOVING --

--AND FEAR. ONCE *FEAR* HAS GOT YOUR SCENT IT'S NEVER FAR BEHIND.

FORCING ITSELF INTO THE MUNDANE.

MAKING IT STRANGE--

--AND TERRIBLE.

BANK

11

HE'S WEAK, AND *DESPERATE* TO TRAIL ME TO THIS DEAD PLACE.

BUT OF ALL THE ABANDONED GHOSTS THAT HAUNT ME --

EEEEEEEE

WHAT'S HAPPENING

PANIC EJECTS ME INTO A FROZEN WORLD --

LOOK AT THE *MONEY,* MAN.

--THAT'S QUICKLY THAWED BY JOYOUS GREED.

GRAB IT!

IT'S JUST BLOWIN' IN THE WIND.

THEY RIP HIM --

12

"BEEN DOWN SO LONG IT LOOKS LIKE UP TO ME."

AGAIN THE NIGHT WAS WRACKED WITH ENDLESS SOBBING--

--BUT THIS TIME IT CAME FROM ME.

KONKRUMMSH

I SHOULDN'T HAVE TO SUFFER THIS. IT'S NOT MY *DUTY*. I DON'T *OWE* ANYONE.

ENOUGH'S ENOUGH.

NO MORE CHOICES.

IT'S OVER.

ONCE I CHOSE TO BE MAGIC'S CONSORT. THEN THERE WAS *PASSION*-- *GOOD* TIMES.

NOW I'M ALL SHAGGED OUT-- GROWN OLD BEFORE MY HOUR.

BUT SHE, CRUEL IMMORTAL, WHIRLS, VIBRANT ON HER WAY--WHILE I FALL PREY TO WELCOME ENTROPY.

JUST LIKE WAITING AT THE DENTIST'S.

LAST FAG. END OF THE LINE.

HOPE IT DOESN'T HURT.

YOU BASTARD.

YOU PATHETIC, WHINING *BASTARD.*

SHIFT UP! I'M KNACKERED. BIN LOOKING FOR YOU ALL OVER.

'STREWTH! YOU SMELL LIKE SOMETHING THE CAT DRAGGED IN.

G-GO AWAY. I'VE GOT NOTHING TO SAY TO YOU.

WELL, THAT'S JUST *TOUGH*, MATE. 'CAUSE *I'VE* GOT *PLENTY*. YOU'RE JUST NOT *ON*, SON--NOT ON AT *ALL*.

IN FACT, YOU'RE A BLEEDIN' *DISGRACE*.

PLEASE, LEAVE ME ALONE. IT'S TOO LATE. EVERYTHING JUST GOT OUT OF CONTROL. I BOLLIXED IT UP.

THE ELEMENTALS, THE CRUSADERS, THE DAMNATION ARMY--IT'S ALL AN IMPOSSIBLE MESS.

THE WORLD'S ON ITS WAY TO HELL-- AND I'LL BE THERE TO MEET IT.

HEROIC BLOODY CAPTAIN GOES DOWN WITH HIS SHIP, EH?

YOU SELFISH, SPINELESS *GIT*. WHAT RIGHT HAVE YOU GOT TO JUST DOWN TOOLS AND *QUIT*?

OK, SO TWENTY YEARS AGO WHEN YOU GOT INTO ALL THIS CRAZY STUFF IT WAS STRICTLY FOR THE LAUGHS--AND SEX.

BUT IT'S NOT A STABLE UNIVERSE, KID, I THOUGHT YOU KNEW!

CHRIST, WHAT AN UTTER *WANKER*. FIRST SIGN OF TROUBLE AND YOU'RE DOWN ON YOUR KNEES LICKING THE DEVIL'S ARSE.

15

THINKING'S LIKE ARCHAEOLOGY. YOU SCRAPE; BENEATH YOUR TROWEL, SHAPE STARTS TO FORM.

FORGOTTEN SECRETS COME TO LIGHT.

'TIL FINALLY YOU REVEAL THE FACE OF PERFECT BEAUTY--

THE PLAN.

IT'S EASY WHEN YOU REMEMBER HOW.

A BACKSTREET CRAP GAME PROVIDES THE CASH FOR CLEAN CLOBBER AND A FLIGHT TO BLIGHTY.

THE OLD, FAMILIAR RUSH IS LIFTING ME -- I'M BACK ON A WINNING STREAK.

IMMIGRATION COULD BE DODGY--I'M BOUND TO BE ON THE SPECIAL BRANCH LIST.

HM CUSTOM
CUSTOMS AND EXIT VI

EXCUSE ME, SIR--

BLEEDIN' TYPICAL, ENNIT? THE ONLY PEOPLE WHO AREN'T AFTER ME ARE THE BLOODY POLICE. I NEED NEVER'VE LEFT THE COUNTRY!

RIGHT, THEN. THE PLAN.

--I THINK YOU DROPPED THESE.

WHA--? OH, TA. WOULDN'T WANT TO LOSE ME DUTY-FREES.

17

GLASTONBURY--WHERE THE CRUSADERS HATCH *THEIR* PLAN.

SHE LIKES TO WALK HERE, ALMOST INVISIBLE IN THE FADING LIGHT. THEY TRUST HER NOW NOT TO RUN AWAY. NOT THAT SHE'D *WANT* TO--

EVEN IF SHE COULD GET PAST THE *WIRE.*

WEEKS SPENT BACK WITH THE CRUSADE HAVE CONVINCED HER THAT THIS IS *RIGHT.* HERS IS THE LIFE MAPPED BY *PROPHECY.*

BUT EVERY NOW AND THEN, MEMORY SLIPS A SUDDEN, UNEASY HAND INSIDE HER WARM CLOAK OF DESTINY--TRAVERSING HER BELLY WITH A SHOCKING TOUCH.

EXCITEMENT. HEARTBEAT. IS IT *HIM*?

NO, JUST A *SCARECROW* GUARDING WINTER WHEAT

TREES MURMUR SECRETS IN THE BREEZE.

POOR JOHN. SHE LOVED HIM, BUT IT COULD NEVER HAPPEN. MAYBE IF SHE'D TOLD HIM *MORE...?*

BUT SHE WAS NEVER THE WOMAN HE KNEW AS *ZED.*

SHE WAS A *CRUSADER*--AND NOT JUST THAT SHE WAS THE *CHOSEN ONE,* MARKED FROM BIRTH TO BE *THE MARY.*

JUST REMEMBER HIM FONDLY AND HOPE THAT HE FARES WELL WHEN THE *NEW JERUSALEM* CONQUERS *HELL.*

HI, KID.

JOHN... HOW DO Y'LIKE MY *TREE* -- COZY, ENNIT?

WHAT...

JOHN, WHAT ARE YOU *DOING* HERE -- I THOUGHT...

WHAT, THAT I WAS *DEAD*, OR *CRAZY?* NAH, NOT *ME*, KID.

SSHHH! QUICK, GET IN HERE. DON'T WANT THOSE BLOODY *DOGS* TURNED LOOSE.

I'VE COME TO BREAK YOU OUT.

NO, JOHN. I'M SORRY, BUT I *CAN'T.* I'VE DECIDED I HAVE TO DO IT. IT'S WHAT I WAS *BORN* FOR.

PLEASE DON'T TRY TO MAKE ME.

NO, DARLIN', I WON'T TRY TO *MAKE* YOU.

HUH, SO I PLAY FALL GUY TO A STARRING ROLE IN "THE SON OF MAN, PART TWO."

DON'T BE BITTER.

I'M NOT. I'D PROBABLY DO THE SAME IF I WERE YOU.

WHAT CHOICE DO YOU HAVE? QUEEN OF HEAVEN OR DRUDGE OF HELL.

DON'T CRY. I'LL *ALWAYS* LOVE YOU, JOHN.

THAT'S GOOD --

--I'LL ALWAYS LOVE YOU, TOO.

19

JOHN...

I'D LIKE TO.

JUST ONCE, THEN?

YES.

ONE LAST TIME, THEN YOU'LL GO.

AND LEAVE ME WITH YOUR MEMORY.

YES.

ALL THE WAY BACK TO LONDON I TELL MYSELF I'VE NO REGRETS.

BY THE TIME I GET INTO THE FLAT, I COULD ALMOST BELIEVE IT'S TRUE--ALMOST, BUT NOT QUITE.

SHE'S GOING TO WANT TO *KILL* ME.

THE ENORMITY OF WHAT I'VE DONE *APPALLS* ME. IF NOT FOR ME, SHE COULD'VE BEEN THE *MOTHER* OF *GOD.*

CHRIST, THAT DEMON'S DEVIOUS. HE KNEW I'D NEVER *KILL* HER.

HE HEALED ME WITH HIS BLOOD JU SO THAT, LOVING HER, I'D *TAINT* HE

--KNOWING THAT NO *ANGEL* WOULD EVER COME WHERE *I'D* SPILLED POISONED SEED.

SO, THE CRUSADERS' *MESSIAH* IS KNOCKED BACK, AND THE *DAMNATION ARMY* HOLDS ALL THE ACES-- NOT GOOD.

UNLESS THE PROPHECY'S FULFILLED BY SOME *NEUTRALIZING* FORCE.

NAH, HE'D *NEVER* WEAR IT -- WOULD HE?

MAYBE IF I *CONCEAL* THE KNOWLEDGE OF THE DEMON BLOOD WITH A *MEMORY- BLOCKING* SIGIL...

TALK OF THE DEVIL.

SHKRIK THRIPP SHUP

200

CHAPTER TWO

L'ADORATION DE LA TERRE

...ETRIGAN!

THEN YOU'RE SURE...?

ONE OF THE INSTRUMENTS IS TAINTED?

NERGAL'S TOUCH AND ACRID SMELL ARE KNOWN TO ALL WHO DWELL IN HELL.

L'ADORATION DE LA TERRE—

RICK VEITCH · writer & penciller – ALFREDO ALCALA · inker – KAREN BERGER · editor –
JOHN COSTANZA · letterer – created by WEIN & WRIGHTSON –
special thanks: JAMIE DELANO

2

SO THIS... MUST BE WHERE... CONSTANTINE LIVES.

ACTUALLY... I'VE NEVER THOUGHT OF HIM... AS HAVING A HOME.

WALKIN' DOWN A ROAD...

WITTA' RATCHET IN YER WAISTE...

HE ALWAYS APPEARED... AND VANISHED SO MYSTERIOUSLY... IT SEEMED THAT HE EXISTED... IN THIN AIR.

BUT NO...

IBM

JOHNNY YOU'RE TOO BAD

THE BOND OF RESPECT... AND CARING... THAT HE HAS FOR THE INHABITANTS HERE... IS UNDENIABLE.

I SENSE THAT THIS PLACE... AND THOSE IN IT... PROVIDE AN IMPORTANT RESPITE... FROM CONSTANTINE'S OTHER... MORE DANGEROUS ACTIVITIES.

A SAFE HARBOR... FROM THE TUMULTUOUS SEAS... HE HAS CHOSEN TO SAIL... IN LIFE.

AMAZING. THOROUGHLY AMAZING.

I'VE KNOWN... JOHN CONSTANTINE... FOR MANY YEARS NOW.

AND I WOULDN'T HAVE THOUGHT... THAT THE CONCEITED SON OF A BITCH... EVER HAD A WARM FEELING... FOR ANYONE.

5

I GUESS I'LL ALWAYS THINK OF THIS PLACE AS MY HOME AWAY FROM HOME.

THAT'S WEIRD...THE DOORBELL DOESN'T SEEM TO BE WORKING.

I'M SURE I OVERHEARD THEM *LAUGHING* IN THERE...

BUT IF THEY'RE 'WAY IN THE BACK ROOM THEY'LL *NEVER* HEAR ME KNOCKING...

NOK NOK

I'LL JUST LET MYSELF IN.

CHESTER! YOU'RE HERE! I WAS JUST ABOUT TO BREAK IN...

ABBY? OH...UH, HI.

HOW YA DOIN'...?

AWFUL! ALEC JUST DROPPED A BOMBSHELL ON ME AND I WANTED TO TALK TO SOMEONE...

TALK? OH, WOW...

LISTEN, I HATE TO *DO* THIS TO YOU, BUT IT'S KIND OF *BAD TIMING* FOR ME RIGHT NOW...

OH. WELL, MAYBE *LIZ*...

ER...UH...WELL, IT'S KIND OF A BAD TIME FOR *HER*, TOO!

I MEAN IT'S A LITTLE WEIRD FOR *BOTH* OF US, IF YOU CATCH MY DRIFT...

OH...OKAY. I UNDERSTAND...

UMM, CHESTER...YOU'RE ACTING *STRANGE!* WHAT'S WRONG...?

NOTHING! NOTHING! IN FACT, IT'S JUST THE *OPPOSITE!*

THINGS ARE FINALLY GOING *RIGHT!*

WITH *WHAT?* YOUR UNEMPLOYMENT BENEFITS? THE ECO GROUP?

NO -- WITH *LIZ!* LAST WEEK SHE FINISHED HER BOOK, AND NOW SHE'S LIKE A DIFFERENT PERSON!

SHE TALKS, SHE LAUGHS, SHE WANTS TO GO OUT -- IT'S *INCREDIBLE!* BUT EVEN *MORE* UNBELIEVABLE IS THAT SHE AND I... THAT IS, ME AND HER...WE'RE, UH...WELL, YOU KNOW...

WELL, LET'S JUST SAY WE'VE REACHED A *CRITICAL POINT* IN OUR RELATIONSHIP!

OH MY GOD! I NEVER THOUGHT IN A MILLION YEARS THAT YOU'D...

AND I INTERRUPTED YOU!? I'M SO SORRY, CHESTER!

IT'S COOL, IT'S COOL...

BUT LISTEN... I GOTTA GO. LIZ IS WAITING, AND "THE FROST IS ON THE *PUMPKIN*" AND ALL THAT...

SORRY I COULDN'T GIVE YOU A SHOULDER TO CRY ON, ABBY!

I'M OKAY, CHESTER. SOMEHOW, KNOWING THAT YOU TWO ARE GETTING TOGETHER MAKES ME FEEL TERRIFIC! 'BYE.

WAIT! WAIT!

WHY DON'T YOU GRAB ALL THIS *MAIL* FROM THE *HOSPITAL* THAT'S BEEN PILING UP? SEEYA!

HOSPITAL? NOW WHAT DOES THE HOSPITAL WANT WITH *ME?*

LOOKS LIKE A BUNCH OF BILLS.

THESE *ARE* BILLS-- FOR *MATT'S* CARE.

WOW! I NEVER KNEW IT WAS SO EXPENSIVE...

BUT THIS IS *CRAZY!* MATT WORKED FOR THE *D.D.I.* THEY'VE ALWAYS PAID FOR HIS HOSPITALIZATION...

MUST BE A COMPUTER ERROR.

KEEP HOUMA CLEAN

THESE DON'T HAVE ANYTHING TO DO WITH *ME.*

OR DO THEY...?

ALEC'S ALWAYS GOING ON ABOUT THE HIDDEN MEANINGS BEHIND *COINCIDENCES...*

MAYBE *THIS* COINCIDENCE WAS MEANT AS A *REMINDER...*

THERE IS SOMEONE WHO OUGHT TO KNOW WHAT ALEC AND I ARE PLANNING...

TERREBON PARISH GENERAL HOSPITAL ENTRANCE

7

THE CAB RIDE TO THE AIRPORT... ALLOWS ME THE LUXURY... OF EXPLORING THIS NEW... *WARMER* SIDE TO... JOHN CONSTANTINE.

JOHNNY BOY! HEY-- I WANT TO *TALK* WITH YOU!

OH, HE'S COOL-- HE'S *SO COOOOL!*

EVEN RUNNING INTO HIS *FUNKY FLASHMAN* DOESN'T FAZE THIS ICE CUBE!

SO HOW'S MY *MULTIFARIOUS MASTER OF MANIPULATION* FARING, EH?

HAH! NOT TALKING!

WELL, I'VE HEARD ABOUT *YOU*, JOHNNY BOY-- HOW YOU'VE GOT THAT *SWAMP THING* CREATURE EATING OUT OF YOUR HAND?

JUST LIKE THE JOHNNY BOY I *USED* TO KNOW...

LISTEN, I'VE GOT MY FINGERS IN A FEW PIES, TOO! I CAN'T NAME NAMES, OF COURSE, BUT DOES *"DARKSEID"* MAKE YOU DROOL LIKE PAVLOV'S DOG?

SO I SAYS TO MYSELF, I SAYS, *"FUNKY, SHOULDN'T YOU AND JOHNNY BOY EXPLORE THE INHERENT POSSI-BILITIES HERE..."*

Y'KNOW... ABOUT ARRANGING A LITTLE *TÊTE-À-TÊTE* BETWEEN OUR BOYS?

WE'LL HAVE TO KEEP IT *HUSH-HUSH*, OF COURSE, AND IT WILL TAKE *TIME* TO PUT TOGETHER SOMETHING *REALLY BOFFO!*

BUT *YOUR* BOY HAS TO WORK HIS WAY UP BEFORE HE GETS A SHOT AT THE CHAMP...

DON'T GET ME WRONG-- YOUR BOY LOOKS *GOOD*, HE LOOKED *GREAT* IN GOTHAM! TOTALLY IN CONTROL...

BUT THE QUESTION REMAINS... HOW'S HE GONNA DO AGAINST SOME *REAL MUSCLE?*

LIKE SAY... *J'ONN J'ONZZ* OR *SUPERMAN?*

SO HAPPENS I'VE KNOWN *LEX LUTHOR* AND *MAXWELL LORD* FOR YEARS!

NOT THAT I'D TRUST THEM WITH THE MILK MONEY, MIND YOU...

BUT MAYBE THEY'D BE INTERESTED, PROVIDED THE CONDITIONS WERE BENEFICIAL TO ALL PARTIES...

BUT WHY... WOULD ANYONE WISH... TO ARRANGE A BATTLE BETWEEN... BEINGS WITH SUPRANORMAL POWERS?

WHY? WHADDYA MEAN "*WHY*"? WHY DOES ANYBODY DO *ANYTHING*?

MONEY! MOOLAH! HARD-EARNED SHEKELS! LEGAL TENDER! FILTHY LUCRE! THAT'S WHY.

THEN IT IS POSSIBLE... TO MAKE A *PROFIT*... FROM THE RESULTING DESTRUCTION?

THE LITTLE PEOPLE, JOHNNY BOY--GOD BLESS 'EM. THEY *LOVE* TO WAGER ON THESE PUNCH-OUTS!

AND SINCE *WE* ARE IN CONTROL, WE NOT ONLY MAKE THE ODDS BUT WE ALSO DICTATE THE *OUTCOME*, SAY NO MORE.

THERE'S THE *BUILDING MATERIALS* ANGLE, TOO!

YOU AND I WILL KNOW *WHICH* CITY IS GOING TO BE KNOCKED DOWN, RIGHT? SO WE CORNER THE MARKET ON WHATEVER PEOPLE ARE GOING TO *NEED* TO REBUILD IT!

THEN THERE'S THE BUTTON AND T-SHIRT MARKET. DON'T LAUGH, IT ALL ADDS UP!

BY THE TIME WE LAND IN WASHINGTON... THIS WARMER VISION OF CONSTANTINE... HAS VANISHED.

REPLACED BY THE SCHEMING MANIPULATOR ...I HAVE KNOWN ONLY *TOO* WELL.

WAITING FOR MY CONNECTING FLIGHT... I PROWL THE STREETS... THINKING OF ALL THE DANGEROUS SITUATIONS ...HE TRICKED ME INTO.

THINKING OF THE WEREWOLVES... THE VAMPIRES...THE GHOSTS... AND EVEN THE TWISTED INVUNCHE.

YOU GET THAT PUG UGLY OF YOURS IN SHAPE, JOHNNY BOY! I'LL BE IN TOUCH!

TATTOOS WHILE U WAIT

GRAB A SEAT, MAC. I'LL BE RIGHT WITCHA...

UNTIL FINALLY... ALL I CAN THINK OF... IS *REVENGE*.

HMMPH.

FZEEEEET!

WHEN I REALLY LOOK AT WHAT I'M DOING, I KNOW IT'S CRAZY.

I MEAN, FOR A NORMAL HUMAN BEING TO EVEN CONSIDER SUCH A THING...

BUT TELL ME ONE THING THAT'S BEEN NORMAL IN MY LIFE, MATT. CRAZINESS JUST FOLLOWS ME AROUND. YOU KNOW THAT.

LOOK WHAT IT DID TO YOU.

BUT THIS TIME... THIS TIME WE'RE GOING TO DO SOMETHING POSITIVE WITH IT. SOMETHING GOOD!

SEE, WE DIDN'T MEAN TO SCREW THINGS UP LIKE WE DID. WE JUST WANTED TO BE TOGETHER, THAT'S ALL.

NOW ALEC SAYS THIS IS A WAY WE CAN SET EVERYTHING STRAIGHT AGAIN.

AND BELIEVE ME, HE NEVER WOULD HAVE ASKED IF HE DIDN'T ALREADY KNOW IT'S WHAT I WANT MORE THAN ANYTHING.

BUT I'VE GOT THIS PROBLEM...

MAYBE I'M OLD-FASHIONED, MATT.

WELL, NOT TO THE POINT OF SACRIFICING REAL LOVE... I MEAN, I HAVEN'T. BUT SOMETIMES... SOMETIMES IT DOES BOTHER ME.

I WALKED DOWN THAT AISLE WITH YOU, MATT.

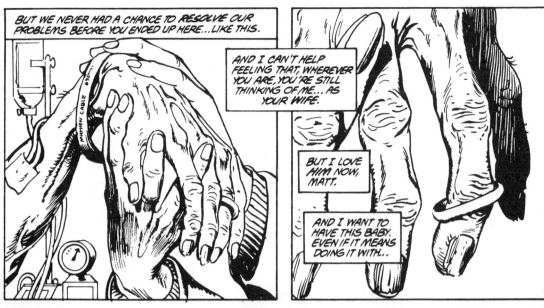

BUT WE NEVER HAD A CHANCE TO *RESOLVE* OUR PROBLEMS BEFORE YOU ENDED UP HERE...LIKE THIS.

AND I CAN'T HELP FEELING THAT, WHEREVER YOU ARE, YOU'RE STILL THINKING OF ME... AS YOUR WIFE.

BUT I LOVE *HIM* NOW, MATT.

AND I WANT TO HAVE THIS BABY. EVEN IF IT MEANS DOING IT WITH...

BING BING

THANKS, MATT.

I KNEW YOU'D UNDERSTAND.

TERREBONNE PARISH RAL HOSPITAL EXIT

AS FAR AS I'VE TRAVELED... WITH ALL THAT I'VE LEARNED... THERE IS STILL MUCH... I DO NOT UNDERSTAND.

I HAVE A PLAN...

I BELIEVE... THAT IT IS A GOOD ONE.

WITH ONE BOLD STROKE... I SHALL NOT ONLY HEAL... THE TARNISHED SPROUT... BUT ALSO BEGAT... A NEW AGE OF ELEMENTALS.

WHY, THEN... DO THESE COLOSSAL EVENTS... SEEM OF SECONDARY IMPORTANCE... TO ME NOW?

PUT PUT PUT

WHY ARE ALL THE SENSES... AND THOUGHTS OF THIS FLESHY VEHICLE... FOCUSED ELSE-WHERE...?

...IN ANTICIPATION.

FOR A BRIEF PANICKED MOMENT... I WONDER HOW CONSTANTINE... WAS ABLE TO HEAL HIMSELF... SO QUICKLY.

WASN'T IT ONLY... A FEW MONTHS AGO... THAT I FOUND HIM... WITH ALMOST EVERY BONE IN HIS BODY BROKEN?

JUST AS SUDDENLY... IT NO LONGER SEEMS IMPORTANT.

NOT AS IMMEDIATELY PRESSING... AS THE DAMPNESS IN MY PALMS... AND IN THE SMALL OF MY BACK.

I FIND MYSELF... LINGERING OUT-SIDE... TRYING TO THINK... OF SOME-THING TO SAY TO HER.

13

HONEY-- I'M HOME!

HUNHH!? OH, IT'S YOU.

YOU SCARED ME, SNEAKING UP LIKE THAT.

GUESS I SHOULD BE USED TO IT BY NOW, SHOULDN'T I?

I'M SORRY... IF I STARTLED YOU. I WAS ONLY TRYING... TO LIGHTEN THINGS UP.

IT IS GOOD... TO SEE YOU AGAIN... MY LOVE, IS EVERYTHING... ALL RIGHT?

YEAH... I'M OKAY. EVERYTHING'S FINE...

GOOD. I WAS WORRIED... THAT YOU MIGHT HAVE... CHANGED YOUR MIND ABOUT THIS. BUT NOW I SEE... YOU'VE BEEN THOUGHTFUL ENOUGH... TO SPREAD SHEETS AND BLANKETS... UPON OUR MOSS BED.

CHESTER MADE ME BUY ALL THIS STUFF AND HAUL IT OUT HERE. I NEVER THOUGHT I'D USE ANY OF IT...

BUT IT SEEMED WE MIGHT BE MORE COMFORTABLE... YOU KNOW, WHEN WE...

I'M SURE... WE WILL BE... VERY COMFORTABLE. BUT WE MUST HURRY... TIME IS OF THE ESSENCE.

I GUESS ALL THOSE COSMIC VARIABLES ARE IN CONJUNCTION, HUH?

NO. YOU'RE OVULATING.

I AM!?

I MEAN-- OF COURSE I AM. IT JUST KIND OF SLIPPED MY MIND, THAT'S ALL...

ALL I SHALL REMIND YOU OF... IS THAT WE ARE ABOUT... TO *CHANGE HISTORY.*

ARE YOU READY FOR *THAT*... MY LOVE?

AS READY AS I'LL *EVER* BE... I GUESS...

THEN LET US BEGIN... WITH A *KISS.*

MMMM

NNNNH

YEEEUCK!

WHAT *IS* IT? ARE YOU... ALL RIGHT? DID I DO... SOMETHING *WRONG?*

YOU TASTE LIKE *CIGARETTES!* BLEEEAUGHH!

I'M NOT KISSING *ANYONE* WHO TASTES LIKE *THAT!*

YOU MEAN... THAT THE *TAR* AND *RESIDUE*... FROM CONSTANTINE'S HEAVY SMOKING... *REPULSES* YOU?

YOU GOT IT.

I'M SURE I CAN MASK... ANY OFFENDING ODORS... BY GROWING A COATING OF CHLOROPHYLL ...IN HIS THROAT... AND LUNGS. HMMMM, HRMMM.

ABBY...IT WILL BE HUMAN...IN EVERY RESPECT...BUT FOR THE *ELEMENTAL POWER*...THAT IT CARRIES.

I'M SURE...THAT I EXPLAINED...ALL THIS TO YOU...BEFORE.

YEAH. I GUESS YOU DID, AT THAT...

YOU WERE *EXCITED*...BY THE PROSPECT *THEN*, ABBY. WHY ARE YOU SO OBVIOUSLY UNCOMFORTABLE...*NOW?*

I *WANT* TO DO IT, ALEC. I *REALLY* DO, FOR *US*. FOR THE *SPROUT*...

BUT WHY DOES IT HAVE TO BE *HIM?*

I *HATE* CONSTANTINE! I *LOATHE* HIM! AND MOST OF ALL...I'LL NEVER *TRUST* HIM.

WHY CAN'T IT BE SOMEBODY *NICE*, LIKE CHESTER OR...

I KNOW--YOU *TOLD* ME-- IT'S ALL PART OF THE *SYNCHRONICITY STORM* YOU STARTED. CONSTANTINE AND I HAVE BEEN DRAWN INTO IT AND SOMEHOW WE *BALANCE* EACH OTHER OUT.

NOW WE'RE PERFECTLY POSITIONED TO TURN ALL THIS *PLANETARY ENERGY* IN A *DIFFERENT* DIRECTION...

ALL WE'VE GOT TO DO IS WHAT COMES *NATURALLY* TO MOST HUMANS...

BUT IT'S NOT THAT EASY FOR ME. SEE, YOU CAN *TELL* ME YOU'RE ALEC, AND I KNOW PERFECTLY WELL THAT ALEC CAN TAKE OVER ANY BODY HE WISHES...

BUT WHEN I *LOOK* AT YOU ALL I CAN THINK OF IS THAT THIS IS ANOTHER OF *JOHN CONSTANTINE'S* DIRTY *TRICKS!*

...AND THAT JUST WHEN I OPEN UP AND ALLOW MYSELF TO BECOME VULNERABLE, THEN YOU'LL SMIRK, AND IT WILL TURN OUT NOT TO BE ALEC, AFTER ALL...

JUST LIKE WITH MATT...

...AND UNCLE ANTON.

18

DAMN! IN MY EAGERNESS... TO PROTECT OUR PLANET... I HAVE ACTED THOUGHTLESSLY TOWARD THE PERSON... I HOLD DEAREST IN ALL THE WORLD.

FORGIVE ME, ABBY, WHEN IT COMES TO... THE COMPLEX INTERPLAY... OF HUMAN EMOTIONS... I AM AFRAID I AM STILL... QUITE *CLUMSY*.

BUT LET ME ASSURE YOU... THAT YOU *DO* HAVE A CHOICE HERE.

IF IT IS TOO MUCH... TO ASK YOU TO GO THROUGH WITH THIS... THEN I CAN RESPECT THAT. SOMEHOW... WE WILL FIND... ANOTHER WAY.

PART OF ME *WANTS* IT. WANTS IT *BADLY.* BUT ANOTHER PART OF ME DEMANDS *PROOF.* SOME SORT OF *GESTURE*, SO I'LL BE *SURE*...

CAN YOU UNDER-STAND?

OF COURSE! AND I'D PROVE IT TO YOU... IN A SECOND... WERE I NOT *CHAINED* TO THIS BODY. TO LEAVE IT PREMATURELY... EVEN FOR A MOMENT... MIGHT MEAN *DEATH* FOR CONSTANTINE.

EVEN *HE* DOESN'T DESERVE THAT, DOES HE?

ABBY... THIS IS OUR *HOME*... OUR SWAMP. PART OF ME... IS IN EVERY LEAF... EVERY FLOWER... EVERY BLADE OF GRASS...

REACH OUT WITH YOUR FEELINGS. YOU'VE DONE IT *BEFORE*... THEY WILL TELL YOU... WHO IT IS THAT STANDS HERE... BEFORE YOU.

I'M SORRY... BUT RIGHT NOW, I DON'T FEEL *ANYTHING* BUT DOUBT AND CONFUSION...

19

THEN PERHAPS... WE SHOULD GIVE IT UP...

LET US HOPE... WE CAN FIND *ANOTHER* SOLUTION...TO THIS QUANDARY... BEFORE IT IS TOO LATE.

IF YOU'RE *REALLY* ALEC...THEN I BET YOU WOULDN'T MIND PUTTING THIS ON YOUR FINGER...

A WEDDING BAND...?

MY LOVE... I WOULD BE...PROUD AND HAPPY... TO WEAR THIS RING.

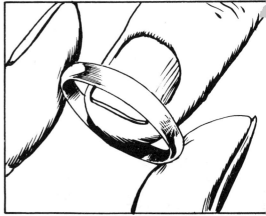

HAHAHA! I *KNEW* IT WAS YOU ALL ALONG!

...IN THE *MARITAL BOUDOIR.*

SIR, TO HEAR THY WRATH, I CHORTLE, SOUND YOU LIKE A NAIVE MORTAL...

DAMN IT! I *REFUSE* TO STAND IDLY BY WHILE FOUL *NERGAL* STRENGTHENS EVIL'S HAND!

SO LET ME BELCH A FLAMING PORTAL...

DEMON-FLAME!? WHAT ARE YOU--?

THAT I MIGHT SHOW YOU THE DOOR!

AT THIS *CRITICAL* MOMENT--YOU'VE TRANSPORTED US TO THE NORTH SLOPE OF HEAVEN!?

CURSED DEMON! WHAT'S YOUR GAME?

I RISK THE PHANTOM STRANGER'S SCOLDING, THAT HE MIGHT WITNESS HANDS ENFOLDING, LIGHT AND DARKNESS, BALANCE HOLDING, ONLY THIS, AND NOTHING MORE.

HEAVEN... YOU'RE OVERSTEPPING YOUR BOUNDS, ETRIGAN.

23

CHAPTER THREE

SEX AND DEATH

MENTED BY A SLOW ...SENTIMENT, MEMORY ...REASSEMBLES.

BLOODY LUCKY I KEPT IT TOGETHER ENOUGH TO GET BACK INTO MY ASTRAL FORM. S'POSE THE OLD DREAM TRAINING CAME IN USEFUL THERE.

THE SUPRA-PHYSICAL REALMS ARE A BIT LIKE DREAMS -- BUT MORE INDEPENDENT.

ACCESSING THE SUB-CONSCIOUS IS THE KEY TO CONTROL.

I AM IN THE *ASTRAL DIMENSIONS* -- ...BUT I'M NOT *DEAD*. HE DIDN'T ...KILL ME -- JUST RIPPED OFF MY ...BODY AND FIRED ME INTO THE ...ETHEREAL REALM, LIKE HE WAS ...TOSSING OUT THE GARBAGE.

IT'S A BIT BLEEDIN' RICH THOUGH, ENNIT? NO WARNING, NO "BY YOUR LEAVE..." I COULD'VE BEEN SCATTERED FROM *ARSE-HOLE TO BREAKFASTIME*.

IT'S NOT EVEN AS IF I WASN'T GOING TO *OFFER*.

I THOUGHT I *WOULD* DO THE GREAT GREEN GILBERT A FAVOR -- A CIVILIZED AGREEMENT BETWEEN *GENTLEMEN*, LIKE.

I LEND HIM MY PERFECT BODY SO HE CAN INDULGE IN A BIT OF RUMPY-PUMPY WITH HIS GIRLFRIEND -- AND HE GETS TO PLANT HIS *SPROUT ELEMENTAL* IN FERTILE EARTH, AS IT WERE.

THE *PROPHECY* GETS FULFILLED. THE RESURREC-TION CRUSADERS GET *STOPPED*. THE *DEMON* GETS IT IN THE EAR. *I* GET THE *CREDIT* -- AND ABBY...

...ABBY GETS *PREGNANT*.

⑦

ZED FEELS DETACHED, ETHEREAL-- AS IF SHE HAD ALREADY MOVED INTO ANOTHER WORLD.

GONE ARE THE YEARS OF CLOISTERED, CRUSADER CHILDHOOD, SPENT IN THE SERVICE OF GOD AND FATHERHOOD.

GONE, THE BRIEF REBELLION OF ADOLESCENCE. SHE HAD SEEN THE WORLD OUTSIDE -- WHERE LOST SOULS BICKER AND FIGHT.

WHERE MEN AND WOMEN MIRE THEMSELVES IN THE WRETCHED CONFUSION OF PHYSICAL LOVE.

GUIDED BY THE HANDS OF WISDOM, SHE HAS RETURNED HOME -- COME AT LAST TO THE PROMISE OF HER DESTINY.

THE PRIESTLY *TONGUES OF FIRE* PERFORM THEIR RITUALS OF ART AND SCIENCE AND THE WORLD QUIVERS WITH THE ELECTRIC HUM OF PRAYER.

THIS IS THE TIME. THIS IS THE PLACE OF PROPHECY.

THEY SEAL HER IN THE CRYSTAL ARK--

THIS IS THE CHILD--OUR DAUGHTER. THIS IS THE WOMAN.

YOU DID THIS, CONSTANTINE. *YOU* KILLED HER-- CONDEMNED HER TO INSANE DEATH, LIKE ALL THESE SORRY BASTARDS.

DONE NOW, THOUGH. HAD TO BE. HUMANITY WOULD'VE BECOME THE SLAVES OF HEAVEN.

DIDN'T HAVE ANY CHOICE, REALLY--

--DID I...?

THAT DEMON'S GOING TO BE ON CLOUD NINE. HE'LL THINK I'VE DROPPED THE WHOLE BLOODY ISSUE RIGHT IN HIS LAP-- FOR A WHILE.

AH, HE'S REELING IN HIS SPY. MIGHT BE ABLE TO FOLLOW HIM OUT OF HERE.

I NEVER ANTICIPATED ALL THIS *DISRUPTION.* I THOUGHT THE ANGEL'D JUST TURN HIS NOSE UP A BIT AND FLUTTER OFF.

13

YOU PLEASE ME, FAVORED THRALL, WHO BRINGS SUCH NEWS TO *NERGAL*.

LISTEN, HEAR VAIN HEAVEN RANT AND SHAKE THE FIRMAMENT.

REJOICE TO THE SWEET SOUND OF ANGELS HOWLING IN THE VOID.

THE PROPHECY IS BROKEN. THE *TONGUES OF FIRE* EXTINGUISHED BY THE PURE WIND OF *CHAOS*.

ALL FALL BEFORE ME.

MY PERFECT STRATEGY HAS BROUGHT US VICTORY. HELL IS ASCENDANT. THIS WORLD IS *MINE*.

CONSTANTINE WAS THE IDEAL WEAPON. CUNNING, RESOURCEFUL--BUT *STUPID*. TRYING TO OUTWIT ME, HE SERVED ME NONETHELESS.

NNNG!

WHAT?

THE "*DRYAD*"? SOMETHING'S HAPPENING IN *THE GREEN*.

14

YAAAAAAH! I KNEW IT. I KNEW IT.

YOU'RE VILE-- FILTHY.

YOU'VE JUST MANIPULATED ME-- USED ME!

YOU SICKEN ME.

UGHH!

I'M SORRY, REALLY. I MEAN IT. BUT I HONESTLY COULDN'T HELP IT.

THIS DEMON WAS CHASING ME THROUGH THE GREEN, SEE --AND I HAD TO GET HELP.

GET OUT OF MY SIGHT. I HATE YOU. YOU BLIGHT EVERYTHING YOU TOUCH.

WELL, THANKS FOR THE MEMORY, DARLIN'.

CONSTANTINE.

REMEMBER NEWCASTLE.

I DO. IT FILLS MY MIND FROM LOUISIANA TO LONDON.

AND ALL THE WHILE I WADE THROUGH SCUTTLING HUMANITY-- FLOTSAM AND JETSAM, UNCONSCIOUS OF THE COSMIC TIDES THAT WASH THEM TO AND FRO.

AM I *INSANE* TO CARE WHAT HAPPENS TO THESE STUPID *SHEEP?* IS IT SOME PSYCHOTIC ARROGANCE THAT DRIVES ME TO SAVE MY SPECIES FROM ITSELF?

IS IT AN IMPULSE OF SELF-DESTRUCTION THAT LEADS ME TO CONJURE DEMONS AND OPPOSE THEM?

OR IS IT *RAGE?*

REMEMBER NEWCASTLE, HE SAID, AND SLAPPED ME WITH A SUDDEN CHILL OF ANGER WHICH NOW GROWS TENTACLES THROUGH ME, LIKE *CANCER,* OR *DEATH.*

REMEMBER NEWCASTLE.

I WOULDN'T HAVE GIVEN HIM CREDIT FOR SUCH SUBTLETY-- BUT THESE TWO WORDS TOUCH ME AS PRECISELY AS A DENTIST'S STEEL PROBING THE EXPOSED PULP OF A MOLAR NERVE.

BUT WHO KNOWS WHAT REFINEMENTS A TORTURER MIGHT BRING TO HIS ART WHEN HE'S HAD ETERNITY TO PRACTICE.

IT'S ALL RIGHT, MRS. M. IT'S ONLY ME.

SNIK

DAMN, BULB'S GONE.

2

--AND ROARS.

WITH ABSOLUTELY NO WARNING, I'M TOTTERING ON THE EDGE OF THE ABYSS.

NAUSEA HAULS ITSELF LUMBERING FROM MY BOWELS --

IN A LANDSLIDE OF UNDERSTANDING, THE WHOLE *WORLD* CHANGES SHAPE.

STRANGELY, IT IS THE GROTESQUE CARNAGE WROUGHT WITH THE CORPSES OF MRS. McGUIRE AND MIGHTY MOUSE THAT ANCHORS ME IN REALITY AS WAVES OF MOTION FLOOD AND PUMMEL ME.

THEN THE APPALLING TRUTH CLEAVES TO ME. HOW DID I NOT SEE IT *BEFORE?*

CHRIST, HE EVEN SPELLED IT OUT, *BOASTED* ABOUT IT-- HE *PLAYED* WITH ME.

NERGAL, NERGAL, NERGAL.

I KNOW YOU *NOW,* YOU *BASTARD!*

23

CLOSED IN THE RUINS OF MY ROOM, IT SEEMS GRAVITY INCREASES ITS GRIP ON ME, FOCUSING ALL MY ENERGY INWARD--

--ENGULFING THE NEBULOUS FIRE OF ANGER IN MY BLACK, PULSATING HEART--

--SQUEEZING IT REMORSELESSLY INTO GLITTERING DIAMONDS OF PURE, MATHEMATICAL FURY.

IT IS AS IF, TURNING OVER A STONE, I HAVE REVEALED THE MEANING OF MY LIFE -- AND THAT MEANING SCUTTLES AND SPITS AND IS CALLED *HATRED*.

AND THAT HATRED IS *UGLY.*

AND THAT HATRED IS *BEAUTIFUL.*

IF HE COULD READ MY MIND--DEMON OR NO-- HE WOULD BE AFRAID.

I OWE HIM A MONSTROUS DEBT, AND I SWEAR--BETWEEN THE DESPAIR OF HEAVEN AND THE HOPE OF HELL--THAT DEBT WILL BE PAID IN *FULL.*

NEWCASTLE 1978

NEXT: *INFERNAL TRIANGLES*

CHAPTER FOUR

INFERNAL TRIANGLES

--AFTER WE'D MADE THE... BABY.

I THOUGHT IT WOULD... BRING US CLOSER THAN EVER... BUT NOW IT SEEMS... I REPEL YOU.

INFERNAL TRIANGLES

JAMIE DELANO guest writer · TOM MANDRAKE guest penciller · ALFREDO ALCALA inker · KAREN BERGER editor

JOHN COSTANZA letterer

3

A MOTH IN THE COOL EVENING, SHE FLUTTERS TO THE WARM CANDLE OF FRIENDSHIP.

CHESTER...? LIZ...?

KNOK KNOK

SHE NEEDS TO TALK WITH HUMANS.

ANYBODY HOME?

BUT FRIENDS CAN BECOME LOVERS.

AND SOMETIMES...

THREE'S A CROWD.

HHAAAHHHH

A-CHOO!

HI, KID.

MY EYES, MY EYES. YOU'VE *BLINDED* ME!

LOOKS LIKE YOU COULD USE-- =ACHOO-- -- SOME HUMAN COMPANY.

THIS IS FUTILE, RIDICULOUS... BUT SOME KIND OF DESPERATE MANIA DRIVES HIM...

GRATEFUL

HE CAN TAKE ANY FACE, PLAY ANY ROLE TO PLEASE HER...

THEN WHO?

MUNDUM'S BAR & GRILL

THIS IS WEIRD. I CAN'T BELIEVE THAT I'M SITTING HERE GETTING DRUNK WITH YOU, OF ALL PEOPLE.

I DON'T EVEN LIKE YOU.

WELL, I HAVE BEEN TOLD THAT I POSSESS AN ALMOST IRRESISTIBL CHARM-- SO DON'T FEEL TOO BAD ABOUT IT--

DON'T BE SO BASE, CONSTANTINE. IT'S THE WAY YOU DRAG EVERY GENUINE, HUMAN FEELING INTO THE GUTTER THAT PUTS ME OFF TO YOU.

'S FUNNY, THAT'S WHAT TURNS MOST PEOPLE ON.

GOOD DROP OF BEER, THIS.

12

PLEASE, JOANY, DON'T GO.

WHAT D'YOU SAY TO A FEW *BEERS*?

YEAH, WHY NOT? I FEEL LIKE GETTING TOTALLY SMASHED. YOU MAY BE A *PRICK*, CONSTANTINE-- BUT YOUR *TIMING'S* PERFECT.

=AA-CHOOO!=

BUT IF SHE DOESN'T WANT *HIM*...

FWPP
FWPP FWPP FWPP
FWPP

YOU PROBABLY CAN'T HELP IT.

ANYWAY, WE'VE GOT A LOT IN COMMON. WE'RE BOTH SMALL-FRY GETTING SCREWED ABOUT BY SUPERNATURAL FORCES OUTSIDE OUR CONTROL.

WHY ARE *YOU* INVOLVED IN ALL OF THIS? WHAT'S YOUR ANGLE?

3

WOOOOO... I CAN'T STOP DANCING -- OR IS IT THE WORLD?

YEAH, THAT *IS* A GOOD DROP OF BEER. I'M SMASHED AS A BLOODY *RABBIT*.

≥HNK!≤ HOW'RE WE GOING TO GET BACK TO HOUMA?

HOUMA? TOO DRUNK TO WALK, THAT'S FOR SURE.

I THOUGHT PER'APS WE COULD STAY HERE, SETTLE SOME OF OUR DIFFERENCES, LIKE...

WELL, I DON'T ≥HNK≤

SSHHH!

OFFICE

≥HNK!≤

≥HNK!≤

≥HNK!≤

OFFICE

JESUS, DID YOU SEE THAT GUY IN THERE -- LOOKED LIKE SOMETHING OUT OF "*THE EVIL DEAD*."

JOHN...

C'MON, WE'RE OVER HERE.

OH WELL, AT LEAST IT'LL KEEP THE RAIN OFF.

JOHN, I DON'T KNOW IF THIS IS A GOOD IDEA.

"JOHN, WILL YOU HOLD ME FOR A WHILE?

"MY HEAD'S SPINNING.

"AND I FEEL LONELY AND A BIT SICK."

ON THE BLUE PLANET, SCULPTING AN ENTIRE TOWN WAS EASY. WHAT'S DIFFERENT NOW?

CAN LOVE BE THE MADNESS...THAT GROWS THESE ABERRATIONS?

OR IS IT... BLIND LUST?

CONSTANTINE...

AND TWISTED JEALOUSY?

BRING HER BACK!

18

RRRIPP

SKASHHRITCH

SKKIDRITCH

HUH... WHERE...?

WHAT... MY RING?

SNFF SNFF COFFEE... AND FLOWERS...?

AND BREAKFAST?

HOUMA DINER

SNIKK

19

MORNING. LOVELY DAY OUT. AND I EVEN REMEM-BERED THE KETCHUP.

CONSTANTINE! HOW... *OWCH!*

OMIGOD! I REMEMBER WE WERE DRINKING AND DANCING -- BUT WHAT HAPPENED?

HOW DID...? I MEAN, DID WE...? STOP GRINNING AND TELL ME.

HMMM, 'S FUNNY, I CAN'T REMEMBER EITHER. MUST'VE BEEN AS PISSED AS YOU WERE.

BUT IF IT'S ANY SORT OF A CLUE--

-- YOU'VE STILL GOT YOUR SHOES ON.

YOU'RE A HARD PERSON TO FIGURE OUT, CONSTANTINE.

TELL ME ABOUT IT. I'VE BEEN TRYING FOR YEARS.

IMPENETRABLE MAN OF MYSTERY, THAT'S ME.

OWW, MY HEAD. WHAT TIME IS IT? ALEC'LL BE WORRIED.

YEAH, WELL, GET THAT BREAKFAST DOWN YOUR NECK-- YOUR TRANSPORT AWAITS.

20

21

"SORRY, WAKE ME WHEN WE GET THERE, THEN."

POP POP POP

POP POP POP

POP POP POP

POP POP POP

POP POP POP

POP POP

22

POPRRRRRRR

BLIMEY, WHAT THE HELL'S HE BEEN UP TO HERE, THEN?

OH, ALEC.

LOOKS AS IF YOUR BOYFRIEND HAD A BIT OF A WILD NIGHT...MUST HAVE BEEN *CROSS* ABOUT SOMETHING.

NO, HE WASN'T ANGRY. JUST *FRUSTRATED.*

OWCH!

HULLO.

23